Collins

Easy Learning

Maths

Age 6–7

My name is ....

I am .... years old.

I go to .... School.

My birthday is ....

Peter Clarke

How to use this book

- Find a quiet, comfortable place to work, away from other distractions.

- Ask your child what maths they are doing at school and choose an appropriate topic.

- Tackle one topic at a time.

- Help with reading the instructions where necessary, and ensure that your child understands what to do.

- Help and encourage your child to check their own answers as they complete each activity.

- Discuss with your child what they have learnt.

- Let your child return to their favourite pages once they have been completed, to play the games and talk about the activities.

- Reward your child with plenty of praise and encouragement.

Special features

- Games: There is a game on each double page, which reinforces the maths topic. Some of the games require a spinner. This is easily made using a pencil, a paperclip and the circle printed on each games page. Gently flick the paperclip with your finger to make it spin.

- Parent's notes: These are divided into 'What you need to know', which explain the key maths idea, and 'Taking it further', which suggest activities and encourage discussion with your child about what they have learnt. The words in bold are key words that you should focus on when talking to your child.

Published by Collins
An imprint of HarperCollins*Publishers*
77–85 Fulham Palace Road
Hammersmith
London
W6 8JB

Browse the complete Collins catalogue at
www.collins.co.uk

First published in 2006
© HarperCollins*Publishers* 2008

12

ISBN-13 978-0-00-730099-0

British Library Cataloguing in Publication Data
A Catalogue record for this publication is available from the British Library

Written by Peter Clarke
Design and layout by Lodestone Publishing Limited, Uckfield, East Sussex; www.lodestonepublishing.com
Illustrated by Rachel Annie Bridgen; www.shootingthelight.com
Cover design by Susi Martin
Cover illustration by John Haslam
Printed and bound in China

Contents

Numbers to 100

Numbers and words

- Write the numbers.

☐ six

☐ fifteen

☐ thirty-eight

☐ seventy-two

- Write the numbers in words.

3   11

40   69

- [ ]

- [ ]

- [ ]

- [ ]

Tens and units

- What is the value of the red digit?

47   12   86   50

☐   ☐   ☐   ☐

- Fill in the missing number.

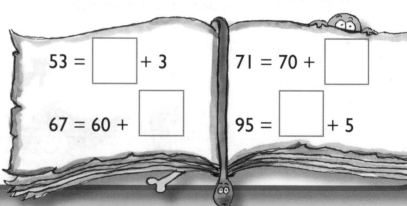

53 = ☐ + 3   71 = 70 + ☐

67 = 60 + ☐   95 = ☐ + 5

What you need to know   At this stage your child is learning to:
- **read** and **write** figures from 0 to 100
- read and eventually write words from **zero** to **one hundred**
- recognise the **value** of each **digit** in a 2-digit **number**, e.g. 47 = 40 + 7 is made up of 40 (or 4 **tens**) and 7 **units** (or **ones**).

Game: Making tens and ones

You need: paperclip, pencil, 20 counters (or buttons).

- Take turns to spin the spinner (see page 2). If it stops on e.g. 6, decide whether the digit will be the tens number, i.e. 60, or the units number, i.e. 6.

- Spin the spinner again. Make that digit the other digit of your 2-digit number.

- The person with the larger 2-digit number wins that round, and takes a counter.

- The first person to collect 10 counters is the winner.

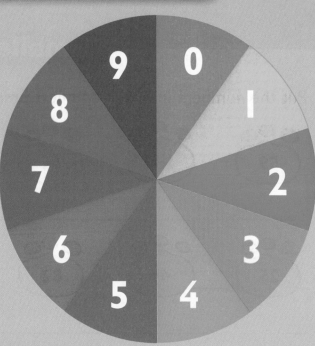

2-digit numbers

- Look at the 4 digits. Choose any 2 to make a 2-digit number.

- How many different 2-digit numbers can you make using these 4 digits?

Taking it further Flick through a book with page numbers up to about 100. Point to a **number** and ask your child to say the number, then **write** it in words. Ask: 'What is the **value** of the first **digit**? And the second?'

Ordering numbers to 100

Smallest first

- Put the numbers in order, smallest first.

| 59 | 42 | 64 | 18 | 73 | 32 |

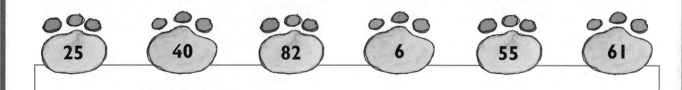

| 25 | 40 | 82 | 6 | 55 | 61 |

| 84 | 31 | 38 | 48 | 13 | 41 |

Largest first

- Put the numbers in order, largest first.

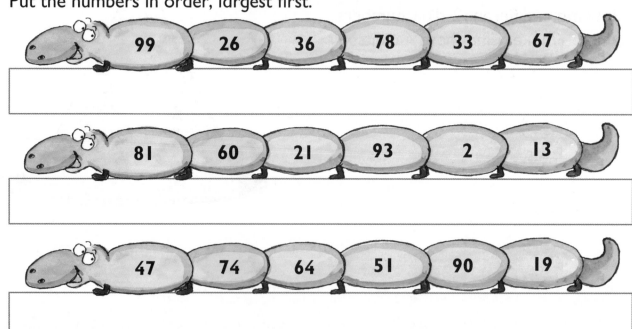

| 99 | 26 | 36 | 78 | 33 | 67 |

| 81 | 60 | 21 | 93 | 2 | 13 |

| 47 | 74 | 64 | 51 | 90 | 19 |

What you need to know Encourage your child to **order 2-digit numbers** by comparing the **tens digits** first. Then, if there are two (or more) numbers that have the same tens digit, look at the **units** (or **ones**) **digits**. A 1 to 100 number grid (see page 9) will help your child understand the number order.

Game: Jungle numbers

40 70 30 50 80
10 90 60 20

You need: 18 counters (or buttons), pencil and paper.

- Cover all the numbers with the counters.
- Take off one counter from each branch, e.g. 40 and 2.
- Write the number as a 2-digit number in the first box below.
- Carry on until you have six 2-digit numbers.

- Now write the 6 numbers in order starting with the smallest.

5 8 4 9 6
2 1 7 3

Ordering 2-digit numbers

- Choose 3 digits. Make 6 different 2-digit numbers using your 3 digits.

- Now rewrite the 6 numbers in order, starting with the smallest.

1 2 3 4 5 6 7 8 9

Taking it further   Point to five of the pawprint numbers on page 6, asking your child to say the **number** and write it down each time. Ask your child to order the numbers from smallest to largest. Then, point to another number and say: 'Where would you put this number so that the other numbers are still in **order**?'

Counting in ones and tens

What comes next?

• Write the missing numbers.

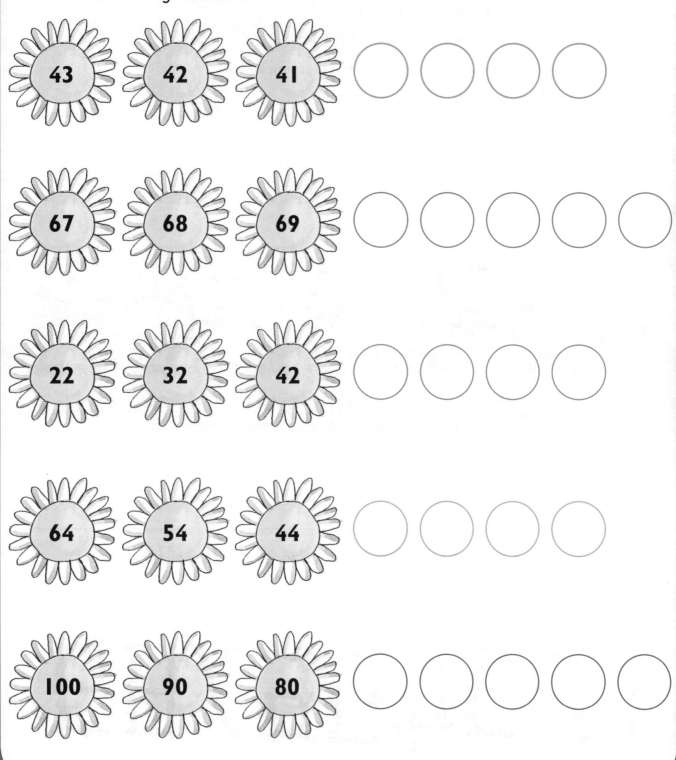

What you need to know At this stage your child is learning to **count on** and **back** in steps of 1, 2, 3, 5 and 10. Being able to count on and back in repeated steps helps your child with addition and subtraction. It is important that when you count **forwards** with your child you do not always start at 0 or 1.

Game: 1s and 10s

You need: 1–6 dice, 2 counters (or buttons).

- Put both counters on 1.
- Take turns to roll the dice and move your counter that number of spaces.
- If you land on:

  a **red** square
  – move **on** 1 space

  a **blue** square
  – move **back** 1 space

  a **green** square
  – move **on** 10 spaces

  an **orange** square
  – move **back** 10 spaces.

- The first player to pass 100 is the winner.

1	2	3	4	5	6	7	8	9	10
11	12	13	14	15	16	17	18	19	20
21	22	23	24	25	26	27	28	29	30
31	32	33	34	35	36	37	38	39	40
41	42	43	44	45	46	47	48	49	50
51	52	53	54	55	56	57	58	59	60
61	62	63	64	65	66	67	68	69	70
71	72	73	74	75	76	77	78	79	80
81	82	83	84	85	86	87	88	89	90
91	92	93	94	95	96	97	98	99	100

Counting on and back

- Write in the missing numbers.

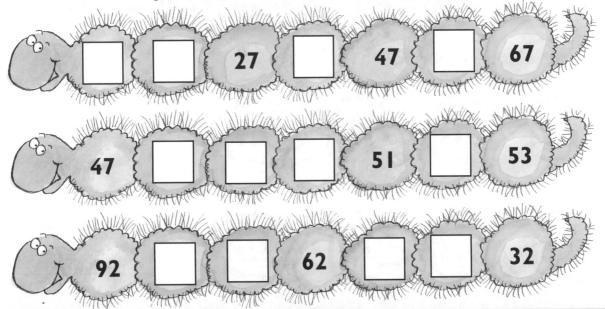

Taking it further   Point to a coloured number on the number grid in the game above, e.g. 4. Ask your child to **count on** in ones from that **number** to the next number *in the same colour,* i.e. 4 to 29. Point to a different coloured number, and ask your child to **count back** to the next number in the same colour. Then point to any number and ask your child to count **forwards/backwards** in tens.

Odd and even numbers

- Circle the even numbers.

8   16   24   25

5   31   37   32

- Now circle the odd numbers.

17   3   21   12

36   25   19   4

What comes next?

- Write the missing numbers.

13   15   17   19   ☐ ☐ ☐

28   26   24   22   ☐ ☐ ☐

What you need to know   Your child is learning to recognise the **pattern** of **odd** and **even** numbers to at least 30. Once they can do this, they should be able to recognise odd and even numbers to 100. Counting on in twos from and back to zero, or any small number, will help your child to see this pattern.

10

Game: Race day

You need: 1–6 dice, coin, about 30 counters (or buttons).

- Put the coin on START. One person is 'even numbers', the other is 'odd numbers'.
- Roll the dice and move the coin that number of spaces.
- If the coin lands on an even number, the 'even' person takes a counter.
  If it lands on an odd number, the other person takes a counter.
- The winner is the person with the most counters when the coin passes FINISH.

START	1			5	6	7				
2	3	4		8			
			9	10	11	12
FINISH						13
30		24	23	22		14
29		25		21	20		16	15
28	27	26			19	18	17

Growing numbers puzzle

- Count the dots in each set.

- Draw the next 4 sets that grow the same way.

- Without drawing them, how many
  dots will there be in the 10th set?
  How do you know?

- What do you notice about the numbers?

Taking it further   From about 30 counters (or buttons), take a handful. Ask your child to count them and put them into 2 equal groups. Then ask: 'Could you do it? Why? Why not?' Repeat several times with other handfuls. Then ask: 'Which numbers can you put into 2 equal groups? What do you know about these numbers? What are the numbers you couldn't put into 2 equal groups called?'

Adding and subtracting to 20

What's the total?

- Answer these. Use the number line to help you.

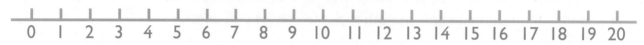

| 0 | 1 | 2 | 3 | 4 | 5 | 6 | 7 | 8 | 9 | 10 | 11 | 12 | 13 | 14 | 15 | 16 | 17 | 18 | 19 | 20 |

$8 + 5 =$ ☐

$6 + 9 =$ ☐

$14 + 3 =$ ☐

$7 + 7 =$ ☐

$3 + 16 =$ ☐

$15 - 8 =$ ☐

$9 - 5 =$ ☐

$13 - 2 =$ ☐

$17 - 4 =$ ☐

$18 - 6 =$ ☐

Totals to 20

- Fill in the missing numbers.

☐ $+ 5 = 17$

$6 +$ ☐ $= 12$

$14 +$ ☐ $= 15$

☐ $+ 8 = 17$

☐ $+ 10 = 14$

$12 -$ ☐ $= 8$

☐ $- 7 = 9$

$20 -$ ☐ $= 4$

$13 -$ ☐ $= 13$

☐ $- 2 = 9$

Game: Add or subtract?

You need: 1–6 dice, 24 counters (or buttons) – 12 of one colour, 12 of another.

- Take turns to roll the dice twice.
- Then decide whether to add the two numbers together, or find the difference between them.
- Put one of your counters on the star with the answer.
- If there is a counter on that star, miss a turn.
- The winner is the person who has covered the most stars.

Magic squares

- In a magic square, each line adds to the same number, across, down or diagonally. This is called the magic number.

Complete these.

Magic number
18

	11	
3		
	7	

Magic number
21

	12	
		8
		9

Magic number
15

4		
	5	
		6

Taking it further Take turns to roll a 1–6 dice. What other number added to the number on the dice makes 10? Repeat 10 times. Extend this activity by making the two numbers add up to 11, 12, 13… Or, say a number between 10 and 20. Then ask your child to roll the dice and say the **difference between** the dice number and your number.

Double and half

Doubling numbers

● Double each of these numbers.

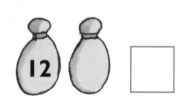

Halving numbers

● Halve each of these numbers.

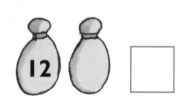

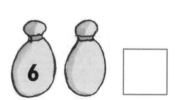

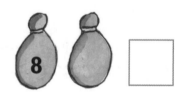

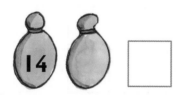

What you need to know At this stage your child is learning to **double** numbers to about 10 and to **halve** even numbers to about 20. Being able to double numbers helps your child when adding and multiplying. Being able to halve numbers helps your child when dividing.

Game: Double or half?

You need: 20 counters (or buttons).

- Use the counters to cover all the numbers on the balls.
- Take turns to remove one counter from a football and one from a beach ball.
- If one of the numbers is double (or half) the other number, keep both counters. If not put the counters back.
- The winner is the person with more counters once all the counters have been removed from the balls.

Number puzzle

- Use each of these numbers once.   1 2 3 4 5 6
- Write them on the kites so that the total on the red kite is twice the total on the blue kite.

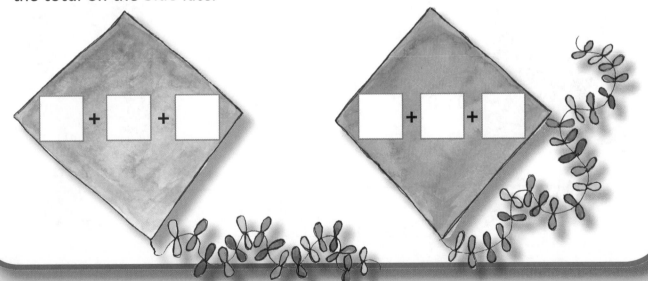

Taking it further Point to each football above and ask your child to **double** that number. Repeat for other numbers using words such as **double, twice, multiplied by 2**. Point to each beach ball and ask your child to halve that number. Repeat for other numbers using words such as **halve, half of, divided by 2**. Then ask: 'I'm thinking of a number. I halve it and the answer is 8. What number am I thinking of?'

2 and 10 times tables

2 times table

- Answer these.

2 x 5 =

6 x 2 =

2 x 9 =

2 x 7 =

3 x 2 =

2 x 8 =

4 x 2 =

1 x 2 =

10 x 2 =

2 x 2 =

10 times table

- Answer these.

2 x 10 =

10 x 5 =

10 x 8 =

3 x 10 =

10 x 7 =

9 x 10 =

4 x 10 =

10 x 6 =

10 x 1 =

10 x 10 =

What you need to know   At this stage it is important that your child knows by heart the 2 and 10 **times tables** as this will help them with their tables up to 10 x 10. Knowing **multiplication** facts will help them to work out related division facts, e.g. 4 x 10 = 40 and 10 x 4 = 40, so 40 ÷ 4 = 10 and 40 ÷ 10 = 4. Being able to count on and back in steps of 2 and 10 helps your child to remember the multiples of 2 and 10.

You need: paperclip, pencil, 20 counters (or buttons) – 10 in one colour, 10 in another.

- Take turns to spin the spinner (see page 2).
- Decide whether to multiply the number by 2, or by 10.
- Find that number and cover it with one of your counters.
- If the number has already been covered, miss a turn.
- The winner is the person with the most covered numbers.

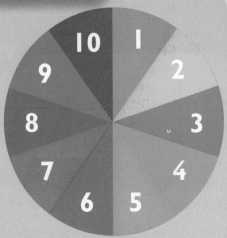

12	10	8	20	4
30	2	60	80	100
16	70	14	6	50
10	40	20	90	18

Multiplication questions

- Use 2 of the numbers and the x and = signs to make some multiplication questions.

Here is one:

- Now answer your questions.

Taking it further Ask your child to count a number of 2p coins, e.g. 5. Then ask: 'So if there are five 2p coins, how much money is this altogether? How do you know?' Show your child how this corresponds to 5 x 2p = 10p. Repeat using other numbers of 2p coins. Then do the same with 10p coins.

Money

What's the total?

- Write the price of each item on the bill.

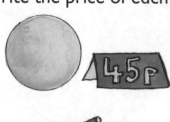    

BILL 1		BILL 2		BILL 3	
ball	....	sharpener	....	eraser	....
pencil	....	ruler	....	toy	....
apple	....	magazine	....	crayons	....
TOTAL	....	TOTAL	....	TOTAL	....

- What is the total of each bill?

How much change?

- How much change from £1 would you get for each bill?

Bill 1 [   ] Bill 2 [   ] Bill 3 [   ]

Game: Totals and change

You need: paperclip, pencil, paper, 10 counters (or buttons).

- Take turns to spin the spinner twice (see page 2).

- Find the 2 items on page 18 and write down their prices.

- Work out the total.

- Work out the change you would get from £1.

- The person who gets more change takes a counter.

- The winner is the first person to get 5 counters.

How would you make...?

- Using some of these coins, can you make all the amounts from 1p up to 20p?

Weights and measures

- Write the weight to the nearest kilogram.

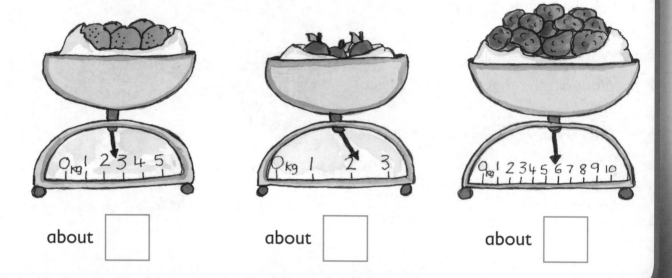

about ☐   about ☐   about ☐

How full is it?

- Colour each jug to show the number of litres on the label.

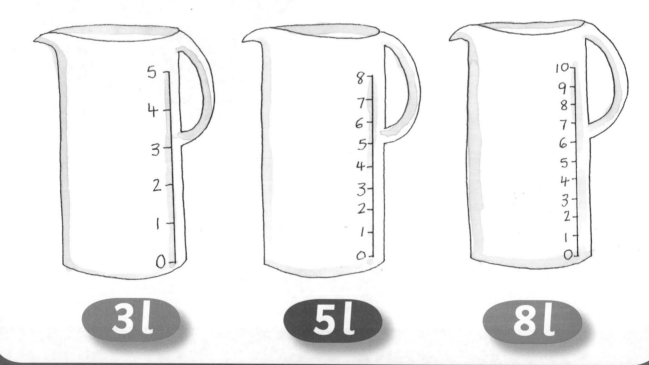

3 l   **5 l**   **8 l**

What you need to know At this stage your child is starting to weigh and measure using standard units of measure, e.g. **centimetre (cm)**, **metre (m)**, **kilogram (kg)** or **litre (l)**. Encourage your child to read scales and to weigh and measure as often as possible.

Game: Weighing and measuring

You need: paperclip, pencil, paper.

- Take turns to spin both spinners (see page 2).
- Find something that weighs or measures what the spinners point to, e.g. 'less than' '1 kg'.

about · more than · less than

1 kg · 1 l · 1 m · 1 cm

Ordering heights and weights

- Write the names in order. Start with the shortest.
- Then put the boxes in order, starting with the heaviest.

Toby is taller than Jeff.

Mel is shorter than Tom.

Tom is almost as tall as Jeff.

Tom's box is heavier than Toby's box.

Jeff's box is lighter than Mel's box.

Toby's box is heavier than Mel's box.

Shortest: 1 _____ 2 _____ 3 _____ 4 _____

Heaviest: 1 _____ 2 _____ 3 _____ 4 _____

Taking it further Ask your child to find something that weighs close to 1 **kilogram**, followed by something that weighs exactly 1 kg. Then find something that weighs about half a kilogram. Check the weight of each item by placing them on the scales. Repeat for containers holding about 1 **litre**, more/less than 1 litre and half a litre.

Using a ruler

Measuring

- Use a ruler to measure the length of each worm.

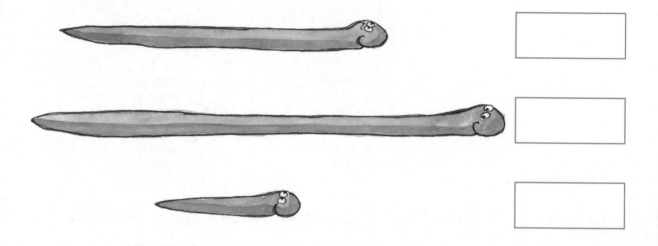

Line lengths

- Use a ruler to draw lines to these lengths.

7 cm

14 cm

11 cm

Game: 30 centimetres exactly

You need: ruler, 1–6 dice, pencil, paper.

cm 0 1 2 3 4 5 6 7 8

- Take turns to roll the dice, e.g. 5.

- Use the ruler to draw a line that measures that number in cm, e.g. 5 cm.

- Each person takes turns to roll the dice and continue their own line, e.g. 5 cm + 3 cm.

- If the roll of the dice makes the line longer than 30 cm, miss a go.

- The winner is the first player to make their line 30 cm exactly.

Twice as big

- Measure each line of this house, and copy it twice as large.

Taking it further Use a **ruler** to draw a straight line for your child which is less than 30 **cm**. Ask them to **estimate** the **length** of the line, before **measuring** it. Then ask your child to draw a line about 30 cm long without using a ruler. Now ask them to measure their estimate using the ruler, before drawing the line accurately. Repeat for different lengths.

Telling the time

- Write the time in words.

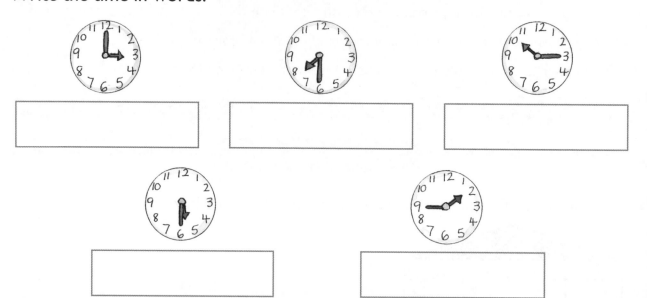

Draw the time

- Draw the hands on the clocks.

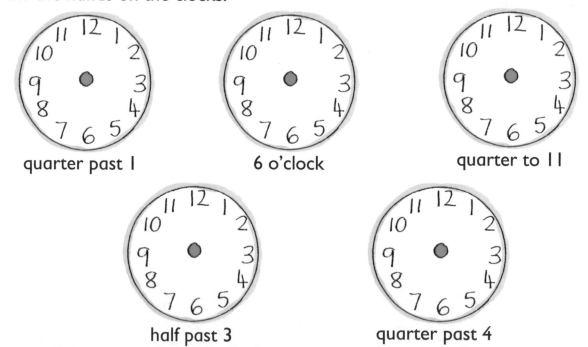

quarter past 1

6 o'clock

quarter to 11

half past 3

quarter past 4

What you need to know   At this stage your child will be familiar with **reading the time** to the **hour** and **half hour**, and will be starting on the **quarter hour**. They will therefore need more practice reading these times. Generally, children find it more difficult telling the time *to* the hour than *past* the hour. It will help if you emphasise the words **past the hour** and **to the hour** and show your child this difference using a clock face.

Game: Time check

You need: 1–6 dice, paperclip, pencil, 10 counters (or buttons).

- Take turns to spin the spinner (see page 2), e.g. quarter past.

- Roll the dice, e.g. 5. You can either keep that number, or double it, e.g. 10.

- If e.g. quarter past 10 is one of the clock times, take a counter.

- The winner is the first person to collect 5 counters.

quarter to   o'clock

half past   quarter past

Digital clocks

- Look at the clocks at the top of page 24. Write each of the times as they would look on a digital clock.

```
3:30
```

Taking it further   Tell the **time** again from each of the **clocks** on these pages. Then use your clock at home to ask 'What time was it … 1/2/6 hours **ago** and **half/quarter** of an **hour** ago?' Then ask: 'What time will it be in … 1/3/8 hour's time, and half/quarter of an hour's time?'

2D and 3D shapes

Flat shapes

- Join the shape to its name.

octagon

triangle

rectangle

hexagon

square

pentagon

circle

Solid shapes

- Join the shape to its name.

cuboid

sphere

pyramid

cone

cylinder

cube

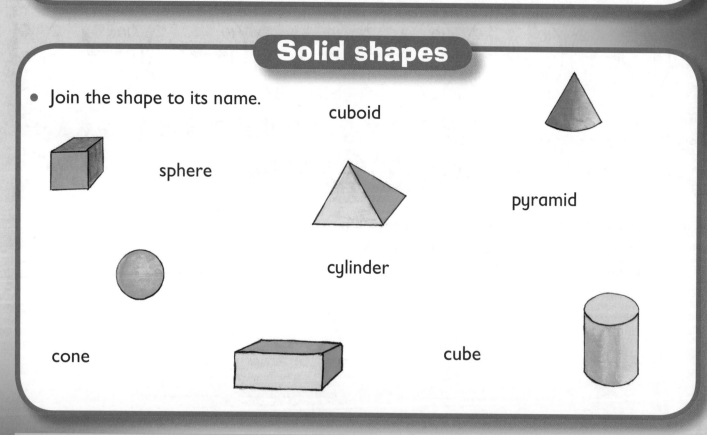

What you need to know At this stage your child is learning to:

- recognise and name simple **flat (2D) shapes**, e.g. **circle**, **triangle**, **square**, **rectangle**, **pentagon**, **hexagon** and **octagon**, and count the number of **sides** and **corners** each shape has.
- recognise and name simple **solid (3D) shapes**, e.g. **cube**, **cuboid**, **pyramid**, **sphere**, **cone** and **cylinder**, and count the number of **faces** (sides), **edges** and **corners** each shape has.

Game: Faces, sides and corners

You need: 15 counters (or buttons).

- Use the counters to cover all the boxes.

- One person takes off one of the counters.

- The first person to name a shape with that number of sides, faces or corners keeps the counter.

- The winner is the player with most counters after all the boxes have been uncovered.

1 side	6 faces	3 corners	4 sides	5 corners
3 faces	1 face	3 sides	4 corners	2 faces
1 corner	6 sides	4 faces	0 corners	8 corners

Estimating sizes

- On a big piece of paper draw each of these objects from memory.

- Try to draw them the actual size.

a 1–6 dice   a tin of tomatoes   a 10p coin   a ruler

- Now compare your drawings to the real thing. How good were you at estimating the sizes?

Taking it further Think of a **2D shape** (see page 26 upper box). Can your child guess your shape by asking questions, e.g. 'Does it have 3 sides? Are its **sides straight**?' You can only answer 'yes' or 'no'. You could also limit the number of questions! Then swap so your child thinks of a shape. Repeat for 3D shapes (see page 26 lower box).

Position, direction and movement

Position

- Shade **blue** every square that is **below** an orange square.
- Shade **green** every square that is **above** an orange square.
- Shade **red** every square that is to the **left** of an orange square.
- Shade **yellow** every square that is to the **right** of a blue square.

Clockwise and anti-clockwise

- Continue these patterns.

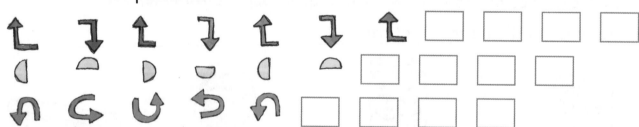

What you need to know   Your child should have lots of practical opportunities to:
- respond to questions or instructions by describing, placing or drawing objects which are in a certain **position**. Use words like **over, under, above, below, on, in, next to, beside, before**
- give directions for someone else to follow to find something. Use words like: **straight, turn, clockwise, anti-clockwise, outside, inside, after, in front of, behind, between, opposite, around**
- talk about and make repeating patterns, and describe what is happening.

Game: Directions

You need: paperclip, pencil, 2 counters (or buttons).

- Place your counters on START.
- Take turns to spin the spinner (see page 2), e.g. 2 down. Move your counter in that direction, e.g. 2 spaces down.
- If you land on a square with points on it, score that number of points.
- If your move takes you beyond the grid, miss a turn.
- The winner is the first person to score 10 points.

Spinner: 1 up, 2 up, 1 down, 2 down, 1 left, 2 left, 1 right, 2 right

Grid:

1 point	football	fish	1 point	present
2 points	penguin	orange	book	2 points
apple	2 points	START	3 points	pencil
coin	1 point	cat	frog	1 point
3 points	car	1 point	banana	dog

Moving in different directions

- Look at the game above.
- Starting at , how would you get to the and win 12 points, passing over these things along the way:

Taking it further Looking at the game above, ask: 'What is to the **left/right** of the coin? What is **next to** the cat? Point to something that is on one **side** of the grid. What is **below** the football? What is **under** the frog? What is **between** the bird and the book?' Then ask your child to choose 2 of the objects and to describe their position in relation to each other.

Solving word problems

- Sam had 7 fish. His Mum bought him 3 more.
  How many fish does Sam have now?

- 8 people are in a train carriage. 7 more get on and 3 get off.
  How many people are in the carriage now?

- Dad buys 5 cartons of orange juice. Each carton holds 2 litres.
  How many litres of orange juice is this altogether?

- There are 2 kg of apples in 1 bag.
  How many kilograms of apples are there in 3 bags?

- Hanna had £1. She bought a bag of sweets for 60p.
  How much money does Hanna have left?

- A cake went into the oven at 2:30. It came out at 3:00.
  How long was the cake in the oven?

What you need to know   At this stage your child is using **mental addition**, **subtraction** and simple **multiplication** to solve 'story' **problems** about numbers in real life, money and measures. Encourage your child to tell you how they worked out the answer. What did they think about? Did they **add**, **subtract** or **multiply**?

Game: Number stories

You need: 1–6 dice

- Take turns to roll the dice twice, e.g. 6 and 2.
- Make up a word problem using your two numbers and either addition, subtraction or multiplication.
- The other person has to work out the answer.

There are 6 apples in the bowl. If Joe eats 2 of the apples, how many are left?

Mum buys 2 egg cartons. If there are 6 eggs in each carton, how many eggs does Mum buy?

Quick quiz

- I think of a number, then halve it.
  The answer is 8.
  What was my number?

- I think of a number, then add 16.
  The answer is 17.
  What was my number?

- I think of a number, then add 5.
  The answer is 12.
  What was my number?

- I think of a number, then double it.
  The answer is 6.
  What was my number?

- I think of a number, then subtract 10.
  The answer is 10.
  What was my number?

- I think of a number, then multiply it by 10.
  The answer is 90.
  What was my number?

Taking it further   Find times at home or when you are out, especially shopping, to ask your child a word problem. Be sure to ask only questions that involve adding and subtracting numbers to 20, and the 2 and 10 times tables.

Answers

Page 4

Numbers and words
6, 15
38, 72
three, eleven
forty, sixty-nine

Tens and units
40, 2, 6, 50
53 = 50 + 3   71 = 70 + 1
67 = 60 + 7   95 = 90 + 5

Page 5

2-digit numbers
12 different 2-digit numbers can
be made:
35, 36, 39, 53, 56, 59
63, 65, 69, 93, 95, 96

Page 6

Smallest first
18, 32, 42, 59, 64, 73
6, 25, 40, 55, 61, 82
13, 31, 38, 41, 48, 84

Largest first
99, 78, 67, 36, 33, 26
93, 81, 60, 21, 13, 2
90, 74, 64, 51, 47, 19

Page 7

Ordering 2-digit numbers
Check your child's answers.

Page 8

What comes next?
40, 39, 38, 37
70, 71, 72, 73, 74
52, 62, 72, 82
34, 24, 14, 4
70, 60, 50, 40, 30

Page 9

Counting on and back
7, 17, 27, 37, 47, 57, 67
47, 48, 49, 50, 51, 52, 53
92, 82, 72, 62, 52, 42, 32

Page 10

Evens and odds
Even: 8, 16, 24, 32
Odd: 3, 17, 19, 21, 25

What comes next?
21, 23, 25
20, 18, 16

Page 11

Growing numbers puzzle

There will be 20 dots in the tenth set.
The numbers are even, multiples of 2.

Page 12

What's the total?
8 + 5 = 13   15 – 8 = 7
6 + 9 = 15   9 – 5 = 4
14 + 3 = 17   13 – 2 = 11
7 + 7 = 14   17 – 4 = 13
3 + 16 = 19   18 – 6 = 12

Totals to 20
12 + 5 = 17   12 – 4 = 8
6 + 6 = 12   16 – 7 = 9
14 + 1 = 15   20 – 16 = 4
9 + 8 =17   13 – 0 = 13
4 + 10 = 14   11 – 2 = 9

Page 13

Magic squares

Magic number 18

5	11	2
3	6	9
10	1	7

Magic number 21

5	12	4
6	7	8
10	2	9

Magic number 15

4	3	8
9	5	1
2	7	6

Other answers are possible.

Page 14

Doubling numbers
Double 8 = 16   Double 6 = 12
Double 2 = 4   Double 5 = 10
Double 10 = 20

Halving numbers
Half 8 = 4   Half 12 = 6
Half 18 = 9   Half 14 = 7
Half 6 = 3

Page 15

Number puzzle

1 + 2 + 4   3 + 5 + 6

Page 16

2 times table
2 x 5 = 10   2 x 8 = 16
6 x 2 = 12   4 x 2 = 8
2 x 9 = 18   1 x 2 = 2
2 x 7 = 14   10 x 2 = 20
3 x 2 = 6   2 x 2 = 4

10 times table
2 x 10 = 20   9 x 10 = 90
10 x 5 = 50   4 x 10 = 40
10 x 8 = 80   10 x 6 = 60
3 x 10 = 30   10 x 1 = 10
10 x 7 = 70   10 x 10 = 100

Page 17

Multiplication questions
Although 20 multiplication number
questions can be made, there are
only 9 different answers, i.e.:
2 x 3 = 6   2 x 10 = 20
3 x 2 = 6   10 x 2 = 20
2 x 4 = 8   4 x 5 = 20
4 x 2 = 8   5 x 4 = 20
2 x 5 = 10   3 x 10 = 30
5 x 2 = 10   30 x 3 = 30
3 x 4 = 12   4 x 10 = 40
4 x 3 = 12   10 x 4 = 40
3 x 5 = 15   5 x 10 = 50
5 x 3 = 15   10 x 5 = 50

Page 18

What's the total?

BILL 1		BILL 2		BILL 3	
ball	45p	sharpener	20p	eraser	10p
pencil	30p	ruler	35p	toy	50p
apple	5p	magazine	40p	crayons	25p
TOTAL	80p	TOTAL	95p	TOTAL	85p

How much change?
Bill 1 = 20p, Bill 2 = 5p, Bill 3 = 15p

Page 19

How would you make...?
1p = 1p
2p = 2p
3p = 2p + 1p
5p = 5p
6p = 5p + 1p
7p = 5p + 2p
8p = 5p + 2p + 1p
10p = 10p
11p = 10p + 1p
12p = 10p + 2p
13p = 10p + 2p + 1p
15p = 10p + 5p
16p = 10p + 5p + 1p
17p = 10p + 5p + 2p
18p = 10p + 5p + 2p + 1p
20p = 20p
You can't make 4p, 9p, 14p
or 19p.

Page 20

How heavy is it?
About 3 kg, about 2 kg, about 6 kg

How full is it?

3l   5l   8l